THE COURAGE TO SAY NO

Twenty-three Songs
for Lent and Easter

John L. Bell
&
Graham Maule

WILD GOOSE PUBLICATIONS
Iona Community
GLASGOW

First Published 1996

ISBN 947988 78 5

© 1996, Wild Goose Resource Group

Design and Illustration
by Graham Maule

The Wild Goose Resource Group has asserted its rights
under the Copyright, Designs and Patents Act, 1988,
to be identified as the author of this work.

Published by Wild Goose Publications

Wild Goose Publications, Unit 15, Six Harmony Row, Glasgow G51 3BA

Wild Goose Publications is the publishing division of the Iona Community.
Scottish Charity No. SC003794. Limited Company Reg. No. SCO96243

The Wild Goose is a Celtic symbol of the Holy Spirit.
It is the trademark of Wild Goose Publications

Distributed in Australia and New Zealand by Willow Connection Pty Ltd,
Unit 7A, 3-9 Kenneth Road, Manly Vale, NSW 2093.
Permission to reproduce any part of this work in Australia or New Zealand
should be sought from Willow Connection.
A catalogue record for this book is available from the British Library.
Printed by The Cromwell Press, Melksham, Wilts.

CONTENTS

INTRODUCTION

Two years ago we published a collection of songs for Advent and Christmas entitled *Innkeepers and Light Sleepers*. This was both for congregational and choral use and has gained wide acceptance.

We were therefore encouraged to look at the possibility of a similar collection dealing with the seasons of Lent and Easter. This book is the result. It has some similarities with the previous publication. For example, the songs do not attach themselves simply to the high point of the season, but are spread out from Ash Wednesday to the Sunday after the Ascension. Too often, Christmas Day and Easter Day benefit from the attention of song writers, but the journey to and from these Holy Days are less well-served with words and music.

Another similarity is that nearly all the songs are arranged in four-part harmony which should be within the reach and compass of most choirs. This is not a selection of test pieces to show the dexterity of the performers. It is an assortment of songs which should be satisfying for choirs and music groups to sing, and yet also provides material which is accessible to congregations.

But there are also dissimilarities.

Innkeepers and Light Sleepers has several songs which may be accompanied on guitar. *The Courage to Say No* has fewer. This is not out of spite either to the instrument or its exponents, but simply because in many songs the harmony changes so quickly that strummed accompaniment would be well nigh impossible. Similarly, there are several songs which, having folk-tune melodies, should not be accompanied by keyboard. A mature and sensitive church musician will discern when to accompany and what to use; a lazy church musician will presume that nothing is possible unless he or she is providing instrumental backing. For countless centuries all that accompanied the human

voice was percussion. People's vocal confidence — contrary to pre-
sumed wisdom — actually increases when they are occasionally enabled to sing *a cappella.*

Another innovation in this collection is the incorporation of songs which come from African and African-American traditions. Our two volumes of World Church Songs, *Many and Great* and *Sent by the Lord,* have opened up for many the rich treasuries of song accessible to us from the repertoire of the churches of the Southern Hemisphere. But if we are really to take such music seriously, it should not simply be published in volumes separate from items of European origin. Here we are glad to incorporate material from Ethiopia, Tanzania, Ghana and Malawi as well as two traditional spirituals.

Few of these songs are contemporary with the publication of the book. The vast majority have been sung, scrutinised and amended several times in the past five or six years and have proven their worth in places far from a printing press.

May Christ, whose ultimate journey they celebrate, use them to God's glory and for the nourishment of God's people.

John L. Bell

Songs
for Lent

The courage to say No

Tune: COURAGE TO SAY NO (JLB)

Quietly and Slowly

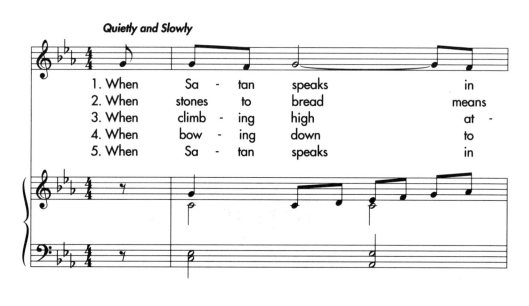

1. When Sa - tan speaks in
2. When stones to bread means
3. When climb - ing high at -
4. When bow - ing down to
5. When Sa - tan speaks in

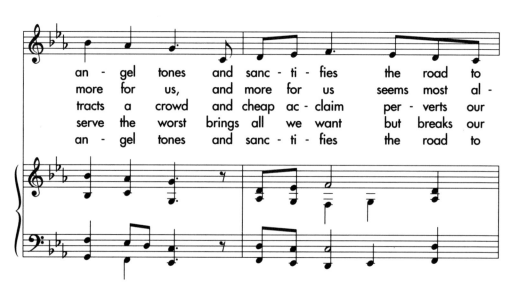

an - gel tones and sanc - ti - fies the road to
more for us, and more for us seems most al -
tracts a crowd and cheap ac - claim per - verts our
serve the worst brings all we want but breaks our
an - gel tones and sanc - ti - fies the road to

10

1. When Satan speaks in angel tones
   and sanctifies the road to ruin;
   if on that path we're asked to go, Oh Jesus,
   give us then the courage to say No.

2. When stones to bread means more for us,
   and more for us seems most alluring;
   if on that path we're asked to go, Oh Jesus,
   give us then the courage to say No.

3. When climbing high attracts a crowd
   and cheap acclaim perverts our calling;
   if on that path we're asked to go, Oh Jesus,
   give us then the courage to say No.

4. When bowing down to serve the worst
   brings all we want but breaks our conscience;
   if on that path we're asked to go, Oh Jesus,
   give us then the courage to say No.

5. When Satan speaks in angel tones
   and sanctifies the road to ruin;
   if on that path we're asked to go, Oh Jesus,
   give us then the courage to say No.

The stories of how Jesus was tempted in the wilderness, stories we associate closely with the season of Lent, are very unique. They could only have come from the mouth of Jesus, as no one else was present to witness what was happening. Their relevance for today becomes apparent when we recognise that Jesus was asked to do things which, to all intents and purposes, seemed right, but for the worst possible motives.

Some poignancy is added to this song if it is sung by three different voices, from different parts of the same building, roughly representing the different venues in which the temptations took place, as well as the different voices of the tempter. The first singer should take verses 1, 2 & 5 and may find it most effective to sing 5 completely unaccompanied, or have the accompaniment fade out mid-verse.

Have mercy upon me, O God

1. Have mercy upon me, O God,
   according to your loving kindness;
   wash from me all my iniquity;
   cleanse me from my sin.

2. Well I know the wrong I've done;
   my sin is always before me.
   Against you only I have sinned
   and done what is evil.

3. You desire faithfulness within,
   so teach me wisdom in my heart;
   purge me and wash me truly clean,
   make me whiter than snow.

4. Let me know the sound of joy and gladness;
   you have crushed, but now may delight me.
   Turn your face from my sins,
   blot out my iniquity.

5. Create in me a clean heart, O God,
   and renew a right spirit within me;
   do not drive me out from your presence
   or take your spirit from me.

6. My God, deliver me from evil
   and I shall declare your salvation;
   Lord, open my lips
   and my mouth shall proclaim your praise.

The Psalm is set to be sung either by a unison voice with keyboard accompaniment, or four–part harmony or both. If voices are singing in harmony, the under–parts simply replicate the rhythm indicated by the small notes of the soprano line.

12

Tune: MISERERE ME (JLB)

1. Have mer - cy up - on me, O God, ac -
cor - ding to your lov - ing kind-ness; wash from me all my in -
i - qui - ty; cleanse me from my sin.

2. Well I know the wrong I've done; my sin is al - ways be -

fore me. A - gainst you on - ly I have sinned and done what is e - vil.

3. You de - sire faith - ful-ness with - in, so teach me wis-dom in my heart; purge me and wash me tru - ly clean, make me whit - er than snow.

14

4. Let me know the sound of joy and glad-ness; you have crushed, but now may de-light me. Turn your face from my sins, blot out my in-i-qui-ty.

5. Cre-ate in me a clean heart, O God, and re-new a right spir-it with-in me; do not drive me out from your

pre - sence or take your spir - it from me.

6. My God, de - li - ver me from e - vil and

I shall de - clare your sal - va - tion; Lord, o - pen my

lips and my mouth shall pro - claim your praise.

Love which understands

Tune: BANCHORY (JLB)

1. O Je - sus Christ, in hu - man flesh you

prac - ticed heav - en's care, be - seiged by need, be -

trayed by greed, sus - tained by faith and prayer.

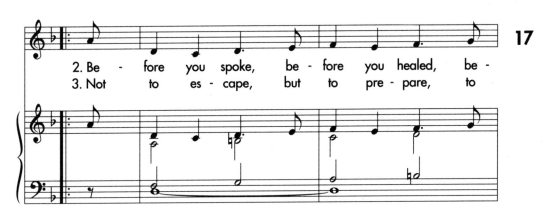

2. Be - fore you spoke, be - fore you healed, be -
3. Not to es - cape, but to pre - pare, to

fore you broke the bread, in crowds, as in the
fath - om and ful - fil, you let your heart and

qui - et place, you felt for where God led.
hands be tuned, in si - lence, to God's will.

Love which understands

18

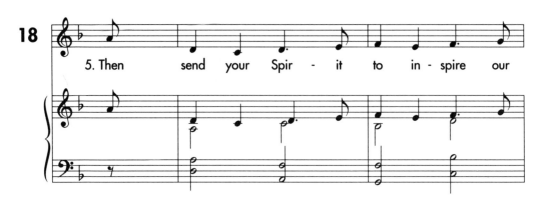

5. Then send your Spir - it to in - spire our

cau - tious hearts and hands, till work and prayer are

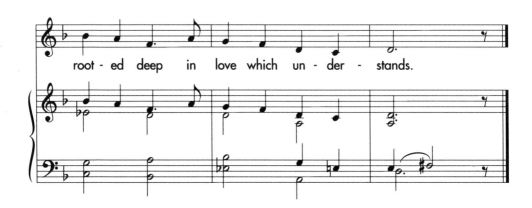

root - ed deep in love which un - der - stands.

Women

4. So we, re-spond-ing to your call to walk your cho-sen

Men

4. So we, re-spond-ing to your call to

Keyboard or Chimes

way, ad-mit our need to learn from you to

walk your cho-sen way, ad-mit our need to

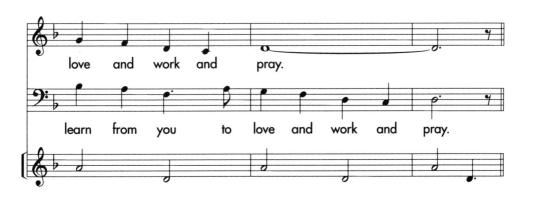

love and work and pray.

learn from you to love and work and pray.

20

1. O Jesus Christ, in human flesh
   you practiced heaven's care,
   beseiged by need, betrayed by greed,
   sustained by faith and prayer.

2. Before you spoke, before you healed,
   before you broke the bread,
   in crowds, as in the quiet place,
   you felt for where God led.

3. Not to escape, but to prepare,
   to fathom and fulfil,
   you let your heart and hands be tuned,
   in silence, to God's will.

4. So we, responding to your call
   to walk your chosen way,
   admit our need to learn from you
   to love and work and pray.

5. Then send your Spirit to inspire
   our cautious hearts and hands,
   till work and prayer are rooted deep
   in love which understands.

The temptations are but one of a sequence of Gospel stories which indicate that, for Jesus, caring was not just a matter of doing, but also a matter of preparing through prayer and reflection. He frequently went to a quiet place to escape the crowds; he encouraged his disciples to emulate his practice; and their failure to do that resulted in their inability to stay watching and praying with him in Gethsemane.

This is essentially a unison song. It may be sung solo unaccompanied, as a duet, or with a choir and congregation.
In event of the last option, the following is suggested:

> v1 Solo voice (with chimes or keyboard)
> 2 Women
> 3 Men
> 4 Choir singing in canon
> 5 All

There are a number of other suitable Common metre tunes, such as *This Endrys Night, St. Columba* and *Gerontius* which can be used as alternatives.

Travelling the road to freedom

Tune: TRAVELLING (JLB)

1. Trav - elling the road to free - dom, who wants to trav - el the road with me?
2. Trav - elling the road to free - dom, who wants to trav - el the road with me?
3. Trav - elling the road to free - dom, who wants to trav - el the road with me?
4. Trav - elling the road to free - dom, I am the Way, I'll take you there.

Fêt - ed by noise and branch - es and ban - ners
Part - nered by staunch sup - port - ers who, come the
Tip - ping the scales of jus - tice, set - ting both
Choose to come on the jour - ney, or choose to

Oh____

hang - ing from ev - ery tree; cheered on by
dark, will turn and flee; nour - ished by
minds and cap - tives free; suf - fering and
crit - i - cize and stare. Earth's mes - mer-

(Oh)

fren - zied peo - ple, puz - zled by what they
faith and pa - tience, nei - ther of which is
yet for - giv - ing, ev'n when my friends most
iz - ing e - vil on - ly a trav - eller

hear and see: trav - elling the road to free - dom,
plain to see: trav - elling the road to free - dom,
dis - a - gree: trav - elling the road to free - dom,
can re - pair. Trav - elling the road to free - dom,

who wants to trav - el the road with me?
who wants to trav - el the road with me?
who wants to trav - el the road with me?
I am the Way, I'll take you there.

24

1. Travelling the road to freedom,
   who wants to travel the road with me?
   Fêted by noise and branches
   and banners hanging from every tree;
   cheered on by frenzied people,
   puzzled by what they hear and see:
   travelling the road to freedom,
   who wants to travel the road with me?

2. Travelling the road to freedom,
   who wants to travel the road with me?
   Partnered by staunch supporters
   who, come the dark, will turn and flee;
   nourished by faith and patience,
   neither of which is plain to see:
   travelling the road to freedom,
   who wants to travel the road with me?

3. Travelling the road to freedom,
   who wants to travel the road with me?
   Tipping the scales of justice,
   setting both minds and captives free;
   suffering and yet forgiving,
   ev'n when my friends most disagree:
   travelling the road to freedom,
   who wants to travel the road with me?

4. Travelling the road to freedom,
   I am the Way, I'll take you there.
   Choose to come on the journey,
   or choose to criticize and stare.
   Earth's mesmerizing evil
   only a traveller can repair.
   Travelling the road to freedom,
   I am the Way, I'll take you there.

The engagement of people in celebrating the season of Lent is often spoken of in terms of a journey. And this is perfectly appropriate, because the intention of Jesus was never to sit still like a guru in a retreat house and have people come and bow at his feet. Rather, he summoned people to follow behind him, and in Lent we are challenged to review how closely we are following, and how far we have moved in our discipleship.

This is a very simple AABA tune which can be sung in unison, but is more effective when harmonised. It may be used as a recessional during Lent and has evident associations with Holy Week.

Where a choir has insufficient altos for the two lines, either sing one alto line, beginning on the F in bars 1, 9, 25, moving to the Eb in the subsequent bars and singing the lower part thereafter; or have a light tenor sing the lower part throughout.

Lay down your head

Tune: RESTING (JLB)

1. Lay down your head, Lord Je-sus Christ, fast falls the
2. All that you've done and all you've said, suf-fered and
3. What lies a-head we fear to guess, you fail to
4. Lay down your head, Lord Je-sus Christ, fast falls the

night. Close fol-low those who crave your end,
shared, proves you're the one for whom the world
fear: hopes seem to fade, heaven seems far,
night. Close fol-low those who crave your end,

28

1. Lay down your head, Lord Jesus Christ, fast falls the night.
   Close follow those who crave your end blinded by sight.
   God give you rest, strength for your task, light for our way.
   Lay down your head and, by your side, we'll sleep and stay.

2. All that you've done and all you've said, suffered, and shared,
   proves you're the one for whom the world waits unprepared.
   Had you conformed, had you condoned, had you complied,
   none would be heard pricing your head, nursing their pride.

3. What lies ahead we fear to guess, you fail to fear:
   hopes seem to fade, heaven seems far, hell seems so near.
   Here, with our faith stretched to the full, put to the test,
   you calmly talk, then kneel to pray, then take your rest.

4. Lay down your head, Lord Jesus Christ, fast falls the night.
   Close follow those who crave your end, blinded by sight.
   God give you rest, strength for your task, light for our way.
   Lay down your head and, by your side, we'll sleep and stay.

It is normally at Christmas, in carols such as *Little Jesus, sweetly sleep,* that we express that kind of close and tender intimacy with Jesus which the Gospels show him clearly expressing to his friends. Often we sing about Christ, but in this song, which is a kind of Lenten evening carol, we sing directly to him.

If at all possible, the song should be sung in harmony and unaccompanied. It has been frequently proven that if a choir or music group sing the first three verses, the congregation, without any rehearsal, can easily join in the final verse.

Songs
for Passiontide

Sing, my soul

Tune: MYSIE (JLB)

Gently

1. Sing, my soul, when hope is sleep - ing, sing when
2. Sing, my soul, when sick - ness lin - gers, sing to
3. Sing, my soul, of him who shaped me, let me
4. Sing, my soul, when light seems dark - est, sing when

faith gives way to fears; sing to melt the ice of
dull the sharp - est pain; sing to set the spir - it
wan - der far a - way, ran with o - pen arms to
night re - fus - es rest, sing though death should mock the

sad - ness, mak - ing way for joy through tears.
leap - ing: heal - ing needs a glad re - frain.
greet me, brought me home a - gain to stay.
fu - ture: what's to come by God is blessed.

1. Sing, my soul, when hope is sleeping,
   sing when faith gives way to fears;
   sing to melt the ice of sadness,
   making way for joy through tears.

2. Sing, my soul, when sickness lingers,
   sing to dull the sharpest pain;
   sing to set the spirit leaping:
   healing needs a glad refrain.

3. Sing, my soul, of him who shaped me,
   let me wander far away,
   ran with open arms to greet me,
   brought me home again to stay.

4. Sing, my soul, when light seems darkest,
   sing when night refuses rest,
   sing though death should mock the future:
   what's to come by God is blessed.

This, essentially solo song, is a paraphrase of a letter from an elderly saintly woman whose testimony is that, even in her lowest days, when she speaks to God he listens, and then she sings to rejoice both her heart and his. It is well suited to the Saturday of Holy Week or to other occasions when loss or weakness are evident.

Behold the Holy Lamb of God

Tumbuka hymn (Malawi)
by Charles Chinula
Trans. by Helen Taylor
Adapt. by Tom Colvin

Tune: HOLY LAMB (arr. JLB)

In stately fashion

1. Be - hold the ho - ly Lamb of God, Ye -
2. In si - lent grief and dig - ni - ty; he
3. And there, out-side the cit - y wall, high
4. But lis - ten to his heart - felt cry, "My
5. Ye - su, while dy - ing on that tree, for -

su, the one who lifts for us a heav - y load.
takes the cross and walks that way to set us free.
on the cross they nail the one who saves us all.
God, my God, now will you leave me here to die?"
gives our fol - ly and our sins and sets us free.

Ho - ly Lamb of God,

RAISED HIGH

ON THE CROSS TO BEAR FOR US THE PAIN AND LOSS.

34

1. Behold the holy Lamb of God,
    Yesu, the one who lifts for us a heavy load.
    Holy Lamb of God,
    RAISED HIGH ON THE CROSS
    TO BEAR FOR US THE PAIN AND LOSS.

2. In silent grief and dignity;
    he takes the cross and walks that way to set us free.
    Holy Lamb of God,
    RAISED HIGH ON THE CROSS...

3. And there, outside the city wall,
    high on the cross they nail the one who saves us all.
    Holy Lamb of God,
    RAISED HIGH ON THE CROSS...

4. But listen to his heartfelt cry,
    "My God, my God, now will you leave me here to die?"
    Holy Lamb of God,
    RAISED HIGH ON THE CROSS...

5. Yesu, while dying on that tree,
    forgives our folly and our sins and sets us free.
    Holy Lamb of God,
    RAISED HIGH ON THE CROSS...

This simple but magnificent song of the passion comes from Malawi. This arragement was made from a very basic transcription which indicated the dialogical nature of the song.

It is particularly effective when used to accompany the procession of the cross into a community gathered for worship on Good Friday. As with other songs from Africa, it can be sung with a cantor and congregation, in unison, or as harmonised above.

When the Son of God was dying

1. When the Son of God was dying, long ago,
   some played dice and some knelt crying, lost and low.
   Cynics sneered and wagged their tongues,
   mockers mimicked funeral songs:
   this, while God's own Son was dying, long ago.

2. Crowds which once had cried, "Hosanna!" lost their voice:
   hell had grinned to hear Barabbas was their choice;
   Judas hung himself for blame; Peter hung his head in shame,
   while the crowds which cried,
   "Hosanna!" lost their voice.

3. Horror, hurt, and pain found home in Mary's breast,
   watching torture's toll and hearing soldiers jest.
   Where was God to hear her cry?
   Why should her own Jesus die?
   Grief and agony found home in Mary's breast.

4. Humankind repeats Golgotha every day:
   God gets gagged while friends and followers turn away.
   Profit threatens peace on earth,
   greed to hunger gives new birth
   as the world repeats Golgotha every day.

5. Jesus, lay your body in this sad earth's grave;
   only one who suffers can presume to save.
   End hypocrisy and lies,
   through our apathy arise,
   bring us the salvation which our spirits crave.

There is a sense in which all the classic hymns of the cross — be they chorales like *O Sacred Head* or spirituals like *Were You There?* — tell the story and little more. Good Friday is not really the time to theologise or work out doctrines of the atonement. It is the time when we recognise, in the people around the cross, something of ourselves; and when we realise that, despite the centuries which intervene, the world still exhibits an uncanny ability to recrucify Christ in the personal and corporate failures to do justly, love mercy and walk humbly with God.

Tune: GOLGOTHA (JLB)

Steadily

1. When the Son of God was dy - ing, long a -
2. Crowds which once had cried, "Ho - san - na!" lost their
3. Hor - ror, hurt, and pain found home in Mar - y's
4. Hu - man - kind re - peats Gol - go - tha ev - ery
5. Je - sus, lay your bod - y in this sad earth's

go, some played dice and some knelt cry - ing,
voice: hell had grinned to hear Ba - rab - bas
breast, watch - ing tor - ture's toll and hear - ing
day: God gets gagged while friends and fol - lowers
grave; on - ly one who suf - fers can pre -

lost and low. Cyn - ics sneered and
was their choice; Ju - das hung him -
sol - diers jest. Where was God to
turn a - way. Prof - it threat - ens
sume to save. End hy - poc - ri -

wagged their tongues, mock - ers mim - icked fune - ral songs:
self for blame; Pe - ter hung his head in shame,
hear her cry? Why should her own Je - sus die?
peace on earth, greed to hun - ger gives new birth
sy and lies, through our ap - a - thy a - rise,

this, while God's own Son was dy - ing, long a - go.
while the crowds which cried, "Ho - san - na!" lost their voice.
Grief and ag - o - ny found home in Mar - y's breast.
as the world re - peats Gol - go - tha ev - ery day.
bring us the sal - va - tion which our spir - its crave.

38 When finest aspirations fail

Tune: APRIL 9th (JLB)

Sadly

1. When fin - est as - pir - a - tions fail and
2. We hurt for what has hap - pened and we
3. Shall they con - trol our des - tin - y who,
4. Oh Christ, you lost con - trol, or so it
5. Then must our hopes, like you, be bro - ken
6. And shall our hopes, like you, a - rise from

dreams be - come dis - may, and all the hopes to -
fear for what's to come; and eas - y con - so -
deaf to our de - mands, are ruled by oth - er
seems, when to a tree they nailed you and re -
down be - yond re - pair; must we be lost and
where they ceased to be; and shall the spir - it

mor - row held lie felled by yes - ter -
la - tion leaves us neg - a - tive and
val - ues and de - fer to their com -
gailed you and re - fused to set you
pow - er - less, be - friend - ed by des -
that was crushed be trans - formed and set

day, what can we do, where
numb, and won - d'ring wheth - er
mands? And are our fu - tures
free; and all be - cause you
pair, in or - der some - how
free? If that's God's will, then

do we turn, what shall we say?
deep - er depths are yet to plumb.
safe in these un - want - ed hands?
·showed how life was meant to be.
to be saved and sense God's care?
we a - wait what's yet to be.

40

1. When finest aspirations fail
   and dreams become dismay,
   and all the hopes tomorrow held
   lie felled by yesterday,
   what can we do, where do we turn,
   what shall we say?

2. We hurt for what has happened
   and we fear for what's to come;
   and easy consolation leaves us
   negative and numb,
   and wond'ring whether deeper depths
   are yet to plumb.

3. Shall they control our destiny
   who, deaf to our demands,
   are ruled by other values
   and defer to their commands?
   And are our futures safe
   in these unwanted hands?

4. Oh Christ, you lost control,
   or so it seems, when to a tree
   they nailed you and regailed you
   and refused to set you free;
   and all because you showed
   how life was meant to be.

5. Then must our hopes, like you,
   be broken down beyond repair;
   must we be lost and powerless,
   befriended by despair,
   in order somehow to be saved
   and sense God's care?

6. And shall our hopes, like you,   **41**
   arise from where they ceased to be;
   and shall the spirit that was crushed
   be transformed and set free?
   If that's God's will, then we await
   what's yet to be.

This is a song to be sung after the remembrance of the cruficixion, perhaps on Holy Saturday. It aims to associate all the brokenness which we experience with the brokenness of Christ, in order that, through him and in imitation of him, disintegrated lives may come together again.

This song was first used, not during Holy Week, but after a staggering blow which a community sustained. In view of this, verse 3 is probably best omitted, if the song is being used at Passiontide.

Thank you for the night

Tune: COMPLIMENT (JLB)

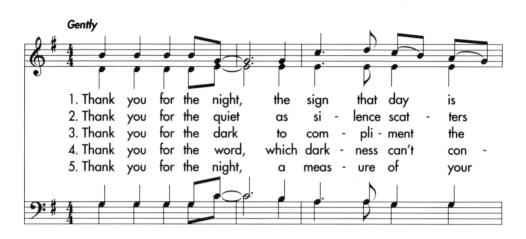

Gently

1. Thank you for the night, the sign that day is
2. Thank you for the quiet as si - lence scat - ters
3. Thank you for the dark to com - pli - ment the
4. Thank you for the word, which dark - ness can't con -
5. Thank you for the night, a meas - ure of your

done, that life is meant to rest and sleep to come.
sound, while God, in both, is wait - ing to be found.
light, as in - sight, o - pen - eyed, re - plac - es sight.
tain, that life, laid down, is raised to life a - gain.
care. In dark - ness, as in light, you, Lord, are there.

1. Thank you for the night,
   the sign that day is done,
   that life is meant to rest
   and sleep to come.

2. Thank you for the quiet
   as silence scatters sound,
   while God, in both,
   is waiting to be found.

3. Thank you for the dark
   to compliment the light,
   as insight, open-eyed,
   replaces sight.

4. Thank you for the word,
   which darkness can't contain,
   that life, laid down,
   is raised to life again.

5. Thank you for the night,
   a measure of your care.
   In darkness, as in light,
   you, Lord, are there.

This gentle vesper may be used at the close of a Good Friday service, or on the eve of Easter, if there is to be no vigil. It is not exclusively for the Easter season, but is most appropriate in this context.

Songs for Easter

Maranatha!

Tune: MARANATHA (JLB)

1. Word of the Fa - ther,
2. First - born of Mar - y,
3. Heal - er and help - er,
4. Ser - vant and suf - ferer,
5. Je - sus, re - deem - er,
6. Christ, res - sur - rect - ed,
7. Ma - ra - na - tha!

COME, LORD, COME AND TAKE OUR FEAR A-WAY, AND TAKE OUR FEAR A-WAY; RE - PLACE IT WITH YOUR LOVE.

1. Word of the Father,
   COME, LORD, COME
   AND TAKE OUR FEAR AWAY,
   AND TAKE OUR FEAR AWAY;
   REPLACE IT WITH YOUR LOVE.

2. Firstborn of Mary,
   COME, LORD, COME...

3. Healer and helper,
   COME, LORD, COME...

4. Servant and sufferer,
   COME, LORD, COME...

5. Jesus, redeemer,
   COME, LORD, COME...

6. Christ, resurrected,
   COME, LORD, COME...

7. Maranatha!
   COME, LORD, COME...

Maranatha is an ancient Aramaic word which means, "Let our Lord come!" It is a prayerful summons to call God into our midst and may be found in 1st Corinthians Ch.16, v.22.

It is therefore an appropriate word to use during an Easter vigil, as the congregation waits for the announcement of the resurrection. The various titles attributed to Jesus can be added to, or omitted, as the situation requires.

For it's best use, the song should be sung just before the announcement of the resurrection is made. The cantor should be at the back of the church, well out of sight. This is a song of communal pleading, not a performance piece.

Jesus is risen, Alleluia!

(Mfurahini, Haleluya - Tanzania)

Text: Bernard Kyamanywa
(trans. by JLB)

Tune: Haya Traditional (arr. by JLB)

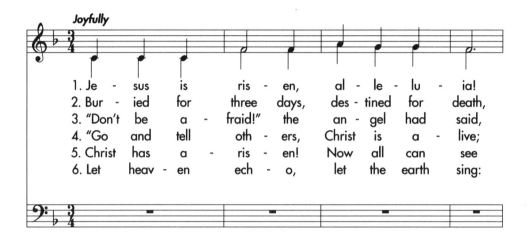

Joyfully

1. Je - sus is ris - en, al - le - lu - ia!
2. Bur - ied for three days, des - tined for death,
3. "Don't be a - fraid!" the an - gel had said,
4. "Go and tell oth - ers, Christ is a - live;
5. Christ has a - ris - en! Now all can see
6. Let heav - en ech - o, let the earth sing:

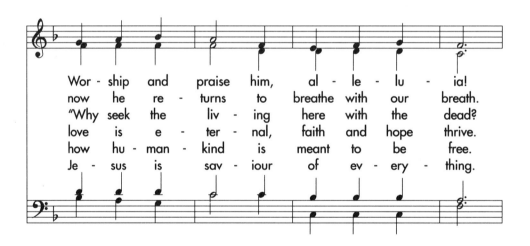

Wor - ship and praise him, al - le - lu - ia!
now he re - turns to breathe with our breath.
"Why seek the liv - ing here with the dead?
love is e - ter - nal, faith and hope thrive.
how hu - man - kind is meant to be free.
Je - sus is sav - iour of ev - ery - thing.

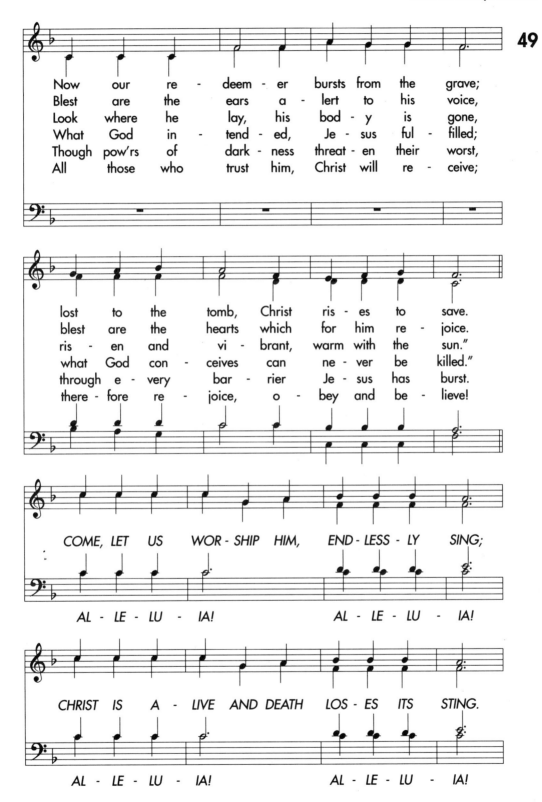

Now our re - deem - er bursts from the grave;
Blest are the ears a - lert to his voice,
Look where he lay, his bod - y is gone,
What God in - tend - ed, Je - sus ful - filled;
Though pow'rs of dark - ness threat - en their worst,
All those who trust him, Christ will re - ceive;

lost to the tomb, Christ ris - es to save.
blest are the hearts which for him re - joice.
ris - en and vi - brant, warm with the sun."
what God con - ceives can ne - ver be killed."
through e - very bar - rier Je - sus has burst.
there - fore re - joice, o - bey and be - lieve!

COME, LET US WOR - SHIP HIM, END - LESS - LY SING;

AL - LE - LU - IA! AL - LE - LU - IA!

CHRIST IS A - LIVE AND DEATH LOS - ES ITS STING.

AL - LE - LU - IA! AL - LE - LU - IA!

50

SINS ARE FOR - GIV - EN, AL - LE - LU - IA!

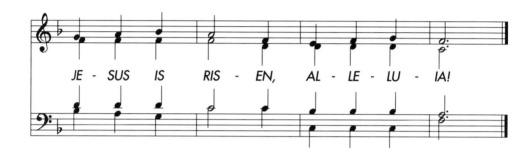

JE - SUS IS RIS - EN, AL - LE - LU - IA!

1. Jesus is risen, alleluia!
   Worship and praise him, alleluia!
   Now our redeemer bursts from the grave;
   lost to the tomb, Christ rises to save.
   COME, LET US WORSHIP HIM,
   ENDLESSLY SING;
   CHRIST IS ALIVE AND DEATH LOSES ITS STING.
   SINS ARE FORGIVEN, ALLELUIA!
   JESUS IS RISEN, ALLELUIA!

2. Buried for three days,
   destined for death,
   now he returns to breathe with our breath.
   Blest are the ears alert to his voice,
   blest are the hearts which for him rejoice.
   COME, LET US WORSHIP HIM...

3. "Don't be afraid!" the angel had said,
   "Why seek the living here with the dead?
   Look where he lay, his body is gone,
   risen and vibrant, warm with the sun."
   COME, LET US WORSHIP HIM...

4. "Go and tell others, Christ is alive;
   love is eternal, faith and hope thrive.
   What God intended, Jesus fulfilled;
   what God conceives can never be killed."
   COME, LET US WORSHIP HIM...

5. Christ has arisen! Now all can see
   how humankind is meant to be free.
   Though pow'rs of darkness threaten their worst,
   through every barrier Jesus has burst.
   COME, LET US WORSHIP HIM...

6. Let heaven echo, let the earth sing:
   Jesus is saviour of everything.
   All those who trust him, Christ will receive;
   therefore rejoice, obey and believe!
   COME, LET US WORSHIP HIM...

This bright tune, with its very straightforward AABA form, sits very comfortably on Western lips, despite originating in Central Africa. This song appears in several versions in Europe and the USA. These are invariably Lutheran publications, Lutherans being a significant denomination in Tanzania.

For reasons of clarity and sensibility, this text does not follow previously published versions, but aims to represent the gist of the original. Similarly, as source documents vary immensely in their arrangement of the tune, the above represents a completely new version, though emulating discernible African rhythmic and harmonic practices.

It can be sung as a choral piece, with the congregation joining the chorus; or as a congregational song in its entirety. If the latter is the case, vary the people or groups singing the verses. People engage more with the text when they don't have to sing every word.

Akanamandla

Tune: South African Traditional

U - Sa - tha - ne.   A –
Sa - tan's had   it!   2. He
Sa - tan's had   it!   3. He

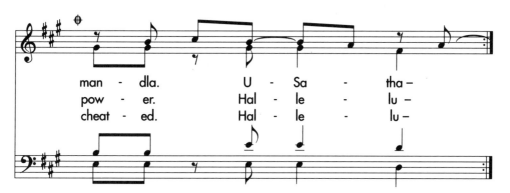

man - dla.   U - Sa - tha –
pow - er.   Hal - le - lu –
cheat - ed.   Hal - le - lu –

U - Sa - tha - ne!
Sa - tan's had it!

si - le.   U - Sa - tha - ne!
from us.   Hal - le - lu - ya.

1. **Akanamandla,**
   Haleluya,
   Akanamandla,
   USathane!

1. **He has no power.**
   Haleluya.
   He has no power.
   Satan's had it!

2. **Simdumazile,**
   Haleluya,
   Simdumazile,
   USathane!

2. **He has been cheated.**
   Haleluya.
   He has been cheated.
   Satan's had it!

3. **Simsabisile,**
   Haleluya,
   Simsabisile,
   USathane!

3. **He flees far from us.**
   Haleluya.
   He flees far from us.
   Satan's had it!

54 *AKANAMANDLA* was one of the first songs from South Africa which was promoted in Great Britain by the Iona Community in the mid 1980's. It came in a collection, *FREEDOM IS COMING,* produced by the Swedish Mission Church and at once became popular as a song of both protest and praise. Like the spirituals, it contains an ambiguity. It sings not only of the triumph of Jesus over Satan, but also of the ultimate triumph of freedom over apartheid, a reality eventually celebrated in South Africa in May 1994.

This song was one which, with others, black people sang in the face of persecution and intimidation at funerals, on demonstrations, in churches. Its full Xhosa text is printed here, but most choirs or music groups may prefer to sing only the first verse in the indigenous language, then sing three in English and return to *akanamandla* for the final verse.

The word *akanamandla* has a popular pedigree in songs of praise and protest in the black church in South Africa. It should be remembered and repeated in all other places where the resurrecting power of God, seen first in Christ, is discerned also in public and political life.

The Lord of all

1. The Bread of Life, the carpenter's own son,
   has made a feast and calls us to his table.
   His food is simple and his words are plain;
   his guests need neither status, rank nor label.
   HE IS THE LORD OF ALL THAT IS
   AND ALL THAT IS TO BE, AND OF ME.
   SO LET YOUR HANDS MEET MINE
   AND SHARE THE BREAD AND WINE THAT SETS US FREE.

2. He is the Alpha and the Omega,
   the King of Love and thus the Prince of Peace.
   What he begins shall never need an end:
   the life he lives is never meant to cease.

3. He is the Servant suffering for our wrong
   and yet the Lord who dances on the grave.
   He helps the weak assist the very strong
   and gives the poor the dignity they crave.

4. Each beating heart, each body and each mind
   are summoned still to answer to his call.
   Whoever yearns for something greater yet
   shall find in Christ the answer and the all.

This very lively song is ideal for celebrations of the eucharist in the weeks following Easter. Being in verse and chorus form, it is helpful to have either a different section of the choir, or of the congregation (men/women/children), sing a verse, with all joining in the chorus.

Tune: LORD OF ALL (JLB)

At a lively pace

1. The Bread of Life, the car - pen - ter's own son, has
2. He is the Al - pha and the O - me - ga, the
3. He is the Ser - vant suf - fering for our wrong and
4. Each beat - ing heart, each bod - y and each mind are

made a feast and calls us to his ta - ble. His food is
King of Love and thus the Prince of Peace. What he be -
yet the Lord who danc - es on the grave. He helps the
sum - moned still to an - swer to his call. Who - ev - er

sim - ple and his words are plain; his guests need
gins shall nev - er need an end: the life he
weak as - sist the ver - y strong and gives the
yearns for some - thing great - er yet shall find in

Dmaj⁷   Dm⁷

nei - ther sta - tus, rank nor la - bel.
lives is nev - er meant to cease.   *HE IS THE*
poor the dig - ni - ty they crave.
Christ the an - swer and the all.

Em⁷   A⁷   D

LORD OF ALL   THAT   IS   AND ALL   THAT IS TO   BE,   AND OF

Gmaj⁷   A⁷/G   Fm⁷

58

ME.   SO LET YOUR HANDS MEET MINE AND SHARE THE

Bm⁷   Em⁷

BREAD AND WINE THAT SETS US FREE.

C   A

To repeat

Final time
rall.

THAT SETS US FREE.

G/A   B♭   Gm⁷   D

rall.

Christ has risen

Tune: TRANSFORMATION (JLB)

1. Christ has ris - en while earth slum - bers, Christ has
2. Christ has ris - en for the peo - ple whom he
3. Christ has ris - en to com - pan - ion for - mer
4. Christ has ris - en and for ev - er lives to

ris - en where hope died, as he said and as he
died to love and save; Christ has ris - en for the
friends who fear the night, sens - ing loss and lim - i -
chal - lenge and to change all whose lives are messed or

60

prom - ised, as we doubt - ed and de - nied. Let the
wom - en bring - ing flowers to grace his grave. Christ has
ta - tion where their faith had once burned bright. They be-
man - gled, all who find re - li - gion strange. Christ is

C   Gm   Gm7   C

moon em - brace the bless - ing; let the sun sus - tain the
ris - en for dis - ci - ples hud - dled in an up - stairs
moan what is no long - er, they ex - pect no hope - ful
ris - en, Christ is pres - ent, mak - ing us what he has

Gm/Bb   F/A   Eb/G   Gm7

cheer; let the world con - firm the ru - mour: Christ is
room. He whose word in - spired cre - a - tion can't be
sign till Christ ends their con - ver - sa - tion, break - ing
been— ev - i - dence of trans - for - ma - tion in which

C   Gm   Am7   Bb

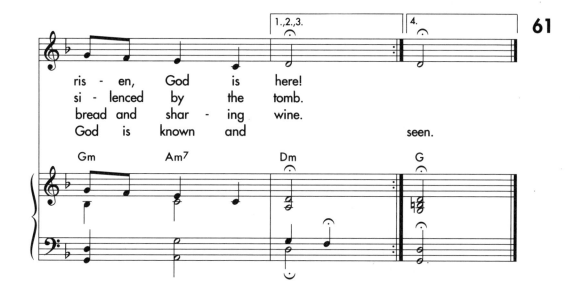

ris - en, God is here!
si - lenced by the tomb.
bread and shar - ing wine.
God is known and seen.

1. Christ has risen while earth slumbers,
   Christ has risen where hope died,
   as he said and as he promised,
   as we doubted and denied.
   Let the moon embrace the blessing;
   let the sun sustain the cheer;
   let the world confirm the rumour:
   Christ is risen, God is here!

2. Christ has risen for the people
   whom he died to love and save;
   Christ has risen for the women
   bringing flowers to grace his grave.
   Christ has risen for disciples
   huddled in an upstairs room.
   He whose word inspired creation
   can't be silenced by the tomb.

62

3. Christ has risen to companion
   former friends who fear the night,
   sensing loss and limitation
   where their faith had once burned bright.
   They bemoan what is no longer,
   they expect no hopeful sign
   till Christ ends their conversation,
   breaking bread and sharing wine.

4. Christ has risen and for ever
   lives to challenge and to change
   all whose lives are messed or mangled,
   all who find religion strange.
   Christ is risen, Christ is present,
   making us what he has been —
   evidence of transformation
   in which God is known and seen.

This is a much gentler Easter song, appropriate for either evening time or for when there is no call for excessive euphoria. This might be the case, for instance, if a death or disaster during Holy Week has stunned a community.

It can be sung solo or by the congregation. In the former case, it might be good to have three different voices taking the first three verses and having either the first voice, or the congregation, sing verse 4.

Oh freedom

1. Oh freedom! Oh freedom!
   Oh freedom over me.
   AN' BEFO' I'D BE A SLAVE,
   I'D BE BURIED IN MY GRAVE,
   AN' GO HOME TO MY LORD
   AND BE FREE.

2. No mo' moanin', no mo' moanin',
   no mo' moanin' over me.

3. No mo' weepin'...

4. There'll be singin'...

5. There'll be shoutin'...

6. There'll be prayin'...

This is one of a number of songs coming from black cultures. *OH FREEDOM!* is reckoned to be one of the earliest spirituals whose origins might well have been in the song of West Africa. The words, which have a hint of the ambiguity embedded in many similar spirituals, are pertinent to Jesus who fulfilled completely the sentiment of the text. Rather than be a slave to sin or Satan, he was crucified, dead and buried. In his death and resurrection, he put an end to the fear of death and rooted Christian worship thereafter in joyful song and prayer.

Opinions as to how the text should be sung vary — as might be expected with music which is essentially in a folk idiom. However these guidelines have held the consensus of several black spiritual singers:

a) a regular rhythm, as expected of a working song, should be present throughout. White choirs, especially in Great Britain, have a tendency to sentimentalise the spirituals by unnecessary and endless rubato.

b) If this were in French, singers would attempt the pronunciation as nearly as they could approximate to the original. Similarly with spirituals, the integrity of the song is respected when the pronunciation of the words, as far as possible, replicates that of native singers. This means that words such as "mo'" should be left without a consonant to end the vowel sound.

c) Normal European practice aims at producing long vowel sounds, with the consonants as precise and clipped as possible. This should not apply to spirituals where an 'm' or 'n' sound is concerned. In other words such as "moanin'" the second vowel should be short and the final consonant should resonate through the singer's head and lips.

Oh freedom

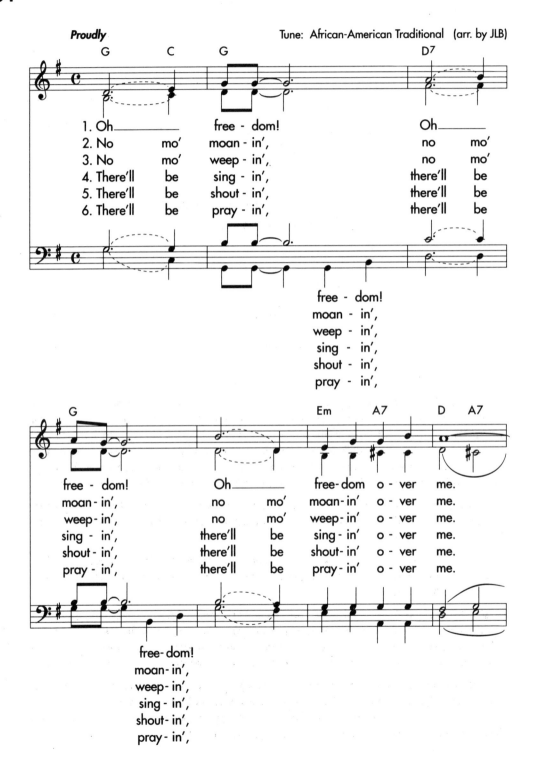

Proudly

Tune: African-American Traditional (arr. by JLB)

1. Oh____ free - dom! Oh____
2. No mo' moan - in', no mo'
3. No mo' weep - in', no mo'
4. There'll be sing - in', there'll be
5. There'll be shout - in', there'll be
6. There'll be pray - in', there'll be

free - dom!
moan - in',
weep - in',
sing - in',
shout - in',
pray - in',

free - dom! Oh____ free-dom o - ver me.
moan - in', no mo' moan-in' o - ver me.
weep - in', no mo' weep-in' o - ver me.
sing - in', there'll be sing - in' o - ver me.
shout - in', there'll be shout-in' o - ver me.
pray - in', there'll be pray-in' o - ver me.

free-dom!
moan-in',
weep-in',
sing-in',
shout-in',
pray-in',

Easter evening

Tune: THE SILKIE, Scottish Traditional (arr. JLB)

Gently

1. As we walked home at close of day, a
2. "Why wan - der fur - ther with - out light? Please
3. We sat to eat our sim - ple spread, then
4. No stran - ger he; it was our eyes which
5. Al - le - lu - ia! Al - le - lu - ia! Al -

stran - ger joined us on our way. He
stay with us this trou - bled night. We've
watched the stran - ger take the bread; and,
failed to see, in stran - ger's guise, the
le - lu - ia! Al - le - lu - ia! As

heard   us   speak   of   one   who'd   gone   and
shared   the   truth   of   how   we   feel   and
as   he   said   the   bless - ing   prayer,   we
Lord   who,   ris - en   from   the   dead,   met
Mar - y   and   our   sis - ters   said,   the

when   we   stopped,   he   car - ried   on.
now   would   like   to   share   a   meal."
knew   that   some - one   else   was   there.
us   when   read - y   to   be   fed.
Lord   is   ris - en   from   the   dead!

68

1. As we walked home at close of day,
   a stranger joined us on our way.
   He heard us speak of one who'd gone
   and when we stopped, he carried on.

2. "Why wander further without light?
   Please stay with us this troubled night.
   We've shared the truth of how we feel
   and now would like to share a meal."

3. We sat to eat our simple spread,
   then watched the stranger take the bread;
   and, as he said the blessing prayer,
   we knew that someone else was there.

4. No stranger he; it was our eyes
   which failed to see, in stranger's guise,
   the Lord who, risen from the dead,
   met us when ready to be fed.

5. Alleluia! Alleluia!
   Alleluia! Alleluia!
   As Mary and our sisters said,
   the Lord is risen from the dead!

This is a second, quieter song, for Easter Day and is particularly appropriate at evening, when the Emmaus road story is recounted.

The tune is probably Orcadian in origin and has a beautiful haunting feel about it, which well matches the words. It is essentially a choral song and, as such, is best sung thus:

  v1 solo voice(s) unaccompanied
  2 solo voice(s) singing text with harmony hummed.
  3 harmony sung
  4 harmony sung
  5 unison for first two lines, harmony for last two.

Songs for the
Post-Easter Period

Tom's song

Tune: LEIS AN LURGHAINN
Scots Gaelic Traditional, (arr. JLB)

Steadily

1. Where they

Oh   Oh   Oh   Oh

Oh   Oh   Oh   Oh

(1.) were, I'd have been; what they saw, I'd have seen; what they
made my de - mand that un - less, at first hand, I could
tales I called lies till his gaze met my eyes, and the
stam - mered, "My Lord!" he re - plied with the word, "Those who
me, ask for proof, sit and sneer, stand a - loof; but be -

Oh   Oh   Oh   Oh

Oh   Oh   Oh   Oh

felt, I'd have shown if I knew what they'd known.
prove what they said, I'd pre - sume he was dead.
words I'd re - hearsed lost their force and dis - persed.
live in God's light walk by faith, not by sight."
lief which is blessed rests on God, not a test.

Oh   Oh   Oh   Oh

Oh   Oh   Oh

"PEACE BE WITH YOU," HE SAID, "TAKE MY
HAND, SEE MY SIDE. STOP YOUR DOUBT - ING, BE -

2. So   I
3. All   their
4. When   I
5. Some, like

Fine   *D.S.*

LIEVE   AND GOD'S   SPIR - IT RE - CEIVE."

Oh

1. Where they were, I'd have been;
   what they saw, I'd have seen;
   what they felt, I'd have shown
   if I knew what they'd known.
   "PEACE BE WITH YOU," HE SAID,
   "TAKE MY HAND, SEE MY SIDE,
   STOP YOUR DOUBTING,
   BELIEVE AND GOD'S SPIRIT RECEIVE."

2. So I made my demand
   that unless, at first hand,
   I could prove what they said,
   I'd presume he was dead.

3. All their tales I called lies
   till his gaze met my eyes,
   and the words I'd rehearsed
   lost their force and dispersed.

4. When I stammered, "My Lord!"
   he replied with the word,
   "Those who live in God's light
   walk by faith, not by sight."

5. Some, like me, ask for proof,
   sit and sneer, stand aloof;
   but belief which is blessed
   rests on God, not a test.

A folk tune conveys the words of this song for the post–Easter period. The words attempt to express the confused and embarrassed condition of Thomas, who was not present when Jesus first showed himself to the apostles after the resurrection. The nature of the tune allows for the melody of the verses, if sung solo, to falter and stumble as the text suggests.

Leis an Lurghainn is usually sung at a brisk pace. However a slower tempo is required for this song. The harmonising parts should endeavour to make their accompaniment during the verses as inobtrusive as possible. Some may prefer to sing "Wo" rather than "Oh", if a slightly more mysterious atmosphere is desired.

You hear the lambs a-cryin'

YOU HEAR THE LAMBS A-CRYIN'
HEAR THE LAMBS A-CRYIN',
HEAR THE LAMBS A-CRYIN';
O SHEPHERD, FEED MY SHEEP.

1. My Saviour spoke these words so sweet,
   O Shepherd, feed my sheep.
   Saying "Peter, if you love me, feed my sheep."
   O Shepherd, feed my sheep.
   YOU HEAR THE LAMBS...

2. O Lord, my love you see and know;
   O Shepherd, feed my sheep.
   Then give me grace to love you more;
   O Shepherd, feed my sheep.
   YOU HEAR THE LAMBS...

3. O wasn't it an awful shame?
   O Shepherd, feed my sheep.
   He hung three days in mortal pain.
   O Shepherd, feed my sheep.
   YOU HEAR THE LAMBS...

Spirituals, as mentioned previously, are work songs. Because of the tender nature of these words, there may be a tendency to sentimentalise, by singing in very hushed tones or making use of rubato. Both tendencies should be avoided. The song can be sung quietly, but it should also communicate the strength, both of faith and of Jesus.

Tune: African-Caribbean Traditional (arr. JLB)

YOU HEAR THE LAMBS A - CRY-IN', HEAR THE LAMBS A -

CRY-IN', HEAR THE LAMBS A - CRY-IN'; O SHEP-HERD, FEED MY SHEEP.

1. My	Sav - iour	spoke	these	words	so	sweet,
2. O	Lord,	my	love	you	see	and	know;
3. O	was - n't	it	an	aw - ful	shame?

hum____

76 What wondrous love is this

Tune: WONDROUS LOVE (U.S.A.)
Southern Harmony, 1835
(arr. JLB)

Moderato

1. What won-drous love is this, O my soul, O my
2. To God and to the Lamb I will sing, I will
3. And when from death I'm free, I'll sing on, I'll sing

soul! What won-drous love is this, O my soul! What
sing; to God and to the Lamb I will sing. To
on; and when from death I'm free, I'll sing on. And

What won-drous love is this, O my soul! What
To God and to the Lamb I will sing. To
And when from death I'm free, I'll sing on. And

What won-drous love is this, O my soul! What
To God and to the Lamb I will sing. To
And when from death I'm free, I'll sing on. And

What won - drous love is this, that
To God and to the Lamb___
And when from death I'm free,___

(for rehearsal)

won - drous love is this, that caused the Lord of
God and to the Lamb, who is the great I
when from death I'm free, I'll sing and joy - ful

won - drous love is this, that caused the Lord of
God and to the Lamb, who is the great I
when from death I'm free, I'll sing and joy - ful

won - drous love is this, that caused the Lord, the
God and to the Lamb, who is the great I
when from death I'm free, I'll sing and joy - ful,

caused the Lord of bliss to
I will sing
when from death I'm free, I'm

bliss   to   lay a - side his crown   for my soul, for my
Am,   while   mil - lions join the theme,   I will sing, I will
be;   and   through e - ter - ni - ty   I'll sing on, I'll sing

bliss   to   lay   a - side   his   crown
Am,   while   mil - lions   join   the   theme
be;   and   through   e - ter - ni - ty

Lord of bliss to lay,   to   lay a - side his crown
Am, I Am, while mil - lions,   mil-lions join the theme
joy - ful be; and through, and   through e - ter - ni - ty

lay   a - side   his   crown
while_____   mil   -   lions   join,
free,_____   I'll   sing   on,

soul, to lay a - side his crown for my soul!
sing; while mil - lions join the theme, I will sing.
on; and through e - ter - ni - ty I'll sing on.

for my soul, his crown for my soul!
I will sing,—————————————— I will sing.
I'll sing on,—————————————— I'll sing on.

for my soul, his crown for my soul!
I will sing,—————————————— I will sing.
I'll sing on,—————————————— I'll sing on.

for my soul, his crown for my soul!
I will sing,—————————————— I will sing.
I'll sing on,—————————————— I'll sing on.

80

1. What wondrous love is this,
   O my soul, O my soul!
   What wondrous love is this,
   O my soul!
   What wondrous love is this,
   that caused the Lord of bliss
   to lay aside his crown
   for my soul, for my soul
   to lay a side his crown
   for my soul!

2. To God and to the Lamb
   I will sing, I will sing;
   to God and to the Lamb
   I will sing.
   To God and to the Lamb,
   who is the great I Am,
   while millions join the theme,
   I will sing, I will sing;
   while millions join the theme,
   I will sing.

3. And when from death I'm free,
   I'll sing on, I'll sing on;
   and when from death I'm free,
   I'll sing on.
   and when from death I'm free,
   I'll sing and joyful be;
   and through eternity
   I'll sing on, I'll sing on;
   and through eternity
   I'll sing on.

This beautiful American folk hymn has a tune which is firmly in the Dorian mode, suggesting a possible historical link with Scotland. The four-part harmony setting may be used throughout, though a more fulfilling rendering could involve a solo voice for the 1st verse, harmony for the second, and unison for the third.

When Jesus Christ worked here on earth

Tune: Almaz Belihu (Ethiopia)
Yemissrach Dimts Literature Program

Howard S. Olson (alt. JLB)

Joyfully

1. When Je - sus Christ worked here on earth, he
1. M - ji - ni kwa - ke Na - za - ret' ka -
2. The el - ders of the syn - a - gogue were
2. Wa - zee wa - li - sha - nga - zwa tu na
3. The way he lived was proof of it: he
4. So pass it on to - day, my friends, the

preached in his home town. I - sa - iah's hopes were
se - ma Ye - su wa - zi. Ya ku - wa kwa - ke
shocked by Ma - ry's son, that he was des - tined
ma - hu - bi - ri va - ke Hu - e - nda hu - yu
'qui - et - ed all strife. The cross it - self he
mes - sage is the same: de - liv - er - ance is

82

now ful-filled, those claims of great re - nown:
u - na - bii. wa ka - le u - me - ti - mi - zwa.
to be-come the Christ for ev - ery - one,
ni na - bii, na ha - ta Kri - sto Ma - si - hi.
could not flee, ev'n though it cost his life.
Christ's to give. For this to earth he came.

Refrain

TO BRING GOOD NEWS TO NEED - Y FOLK, TO
KU - SA - I - DI - A MA - SKI - NI, VI -

HELP THE BLIND TO SEE, TO HEAL THE BRO - KEN
PO - FU NA - O WA - O - NE. WA - FU - NGWA WA - WE

HEARTS A - GAIN AND SET THE CAP - TIVES FREE. TO
HU - RU TU WA - SE - TWA WA - WE WA - ZI - MA. KU -

BRING GOOD NEWS TO NEED - Y FOLK, TO
SA - I - DI - A MA - SKI - NI, VI -

TO BRING GOOD NEWS TO
MA - SKI - NI, WO - TE

HELP THE BLIND TO SEE, TO HEAL THE BRO - KEN
PO - FU NA - O WA - O - NE. WA - FU - NGWA WA - WE

ALL
WA - O - NE. WA

BLIND TO SEE, TO

HEARTS A - GAIN AND SET THE CAP - TIVES FREE.
HU - RU TU WA - SE - TWA WA - WE WA - ZI - MA.

84

1. When Jesus Christ worked here on earth,
   he preached in his home town.
   Isaiah's hopes were now fulfilled,
   those claims of great renown:

   TO BRING GOOD NEWS TO NEEDY FOLK,
   TO HELP THE BLIND TO SEE,
   TO HEAL THE BROKEN HEARTS AGAIN,
   AND SET THE CAPTIVES FREE. (repeat)

2. The elders of the synagogue
   were shocked by Mary's son,
   that he was destined to become
   the Christ for everyone,

3. The way he lived was proof of it:
   he quieted all strife.
   The cross itself he could not flee,
   ev'n though it cost his life.

4. So pass it on today, my friends,
   the message is the same:
   deliverance is Christ's to give.
   For this to earth he came.

1. Mjini kwake Nazaret'
   kasema Yesu wazi.
   Ya kuwa kwake unabii.
   wa kale umetimizwa.

   KUSAIDIA MASKINI,
   VIPOFU NAO WAONE.
   WAFUNGWA WAWE HURU TU,
   WASETWA WAWE WAZIMA. (repeat)

2. Wazee walishangazwa tu
   na mahubiri vake
   Huenda huyu ni nabii,
   na hata Kristo Masihi.

African religious songs frequently do what European songs don't — they tell the story of biblical people and are thus both educational and evangelical.

This song comes from Ethiopia and appeared in the Northern Hemisphere translated by Howard S. Olson in a collection entitled *SET FREE*, published by Ausburg Fortress, Minneapolis.

When our master Jesus went away

A teaching song by Tom Colvin
for the Church at Nyohene, Ghana

Tune: NYOHENE
Ghanian Traditional (arr. JLB)

Gently but brightly

1. When our mas-ter Je - sus went a - way,
2. In all Je - sus' friends the Spir - it lives;
3. God the Spir - it tells us what to say,
4. God the Spir - it shows us where to go,
5. God the Spir - it fills us with his love,
6. God the Spir - it fills the Church on earth,
7. Spir - it of our God and God's own Son,

1. When our mas - ter Je - sus went a - way,
2. In all Je - sus' friends the Spir - it lives;
3. God the Spir - it tells us what to say,
4. God the Spir - it shows us where to go,
5. God the Spir - it fills us with his love,
6. God the Spir - it fills the Church on earth,
7. Spir - it of our God and God's own Son,

he prom-ised a friend with us to stay.
and, by Je - sus' power, he helps and saves.
when our crit - ics scorn Christ's cho - sen way.
when the Sav - iour's will we seek to know.
meant for hu - man - kind, from God a - bove.
bring-ing ev - ery bap - tised soul new birth.
you, with them, we praise, for - ev - er one.

he prom - ised a friend with us to stay.
and, by Je - sus' power, he helps and saves.
when our crit - ics scorn Christ's cho - sen way.
when the Sav - iour's will we seek to know.
meant for hu - man-kind, from God a - bove.
bring - ing ev - ery bap - tised soul new birth.
you, with them, we praise, for - ev - er one.

COME, GUIDE ON EARTH OUR SPIR - IT-FRIEND; COME

TO IN - SPIRE, DI - RECT AND DE - FEND.

88

1. When our master Jesus went away,
   he promised a friend with us to stay.
   COME, GUIDE ON EARTH OUR SPIRIT-FRIEND;
   COME TO INSPIRE, DIRECT AND DEFEND.

2. In all Jesus' friends the Spirit lives;
   and, by Jesus' power, he helps and saves.
   COME, GUIDE ON EARTH...

3. God the Spirit tells us what to say,
   when our critics scorn Christ's chosen way.
   COME, GUIDE ON EARTH...

4. God the Spirit shows us where to go,
   when the Saviour's will we seek to know.
   COME, GUIDE ON EARTH...

5. God the Spirit fills us with his love,
   meant for humankind, from God above.
   COME, GUIDE ON EARTH...

6. God the Spirit fills the Church on earth,
   bringing every baptised soul new birth.
   COME, GUIDE ON EARTH...

7. Spirit of our God and God's own Son,
   you, with them, we praise, forever one.
   COME, GUIDE ON EARTH...

This is another of the melodies from Northern Ghana collected, by Tom Colvin, from the singing of people at village ceilidhs (concerts). Tom Colvin wrote these words to the melody for the new Church at Nyohene, Ghana.

This lovely song both re–tells the promise of Christ, and invokes the Spirit. It has been slightly amended in rhythm and has been harmonised. Little has been altered in the original text. However, if people feel uncomfortable with "master Jesus," it is easy to substitute "saviour Jesus." And if people are reticent to call the Spirit "he" it is quite acceptable to change that to "she." In different languages the Spirit is given different genders, and in some African tongues, the same word is used for "he" and "she."

Verses may be omitted ad lib.

Other songs from Africa, collected by Tom Colvin, are found in *FILL US WITH YOUR LOVE*, published in 1983 by Agape, Illinois.

Holy forever

Tune: COLBOOTH (JLB)

Brightly

1. Ho - ly for - ev - er and ev - er is God,
2. Praise to our Mak - er and Mov - er we sing,
3. Wor - thy are you who, by shed - ding your blood,
4. Wor - thy the Lamb who was sen - tenced and slain!
5. Bless - ing and hon - our and glo - ry and might

o - ver all crea - tures the sov - er - eign Lord,
glo - ry and hon - our and bless - ing we bring;
brought from all na - tions a peo - ple for God.
Wor - thy the Lamb in his ris - ing a - gain!
be to the Lamb on the throne, as is right.

Ped.

who was, and is, and who is yet to come. Al - le - lu -
all our ex - is - tence de - pends on the Lord. Al - le - lu -
Folk of all rac - es you call to be priests. Al - le - lu -
Wor - thy of pow - er and wis - dom and wealth, Al - le - lu -
Let earth and heav - en u - nite to ex - claim Al - le - lu -

Last time

ia!
ia!
ia!
ia!
ia!   A - men.

92

1. Holy forever and ever is God,
   over all creatures the sovereign Lord,
   who was, and is, and who is yet to come.
   Alleluia!

2. Praise to our Maker and Mover we sing,
   glory and honour and blessing we bring;
   all our existence depends on the Lord.
   Alleluia!

3. Worthy are you who, by shedding your blood,
   brought from all nations a people for God.
   Folk of all races you call to be priests.
   Alleluia!

4. Worthy the Lamb who was sentenced and slain!
   Worthy the Lamb in his rising again!
   Worthy of power and wisdom and wealth,
   Alleluia!

5. Blessing and honour and glory and might
   be to the Lamb on the throne, as is right.
   Let earth and heaven unite to exclaim
   Alleluia! Amen.

In the Book of Revelation, we are given an insight into the worship of heaven in which Christ shares since, after his ascension, he is seated at God's right hand.

This paraphrase of words from chapter five should be sung in unison and with organ accompaniment.

Index of first lines (alphabetical)

The Iona Community

The Iona Community was founded in 1938 by the late Lord MacLeod of Fuinary (the Rev. George MacLeod DD). It was initially a movement for renewal in the Church of Scotland. The rebuilding of the ruined cloistral buildings of Iona Abbey (completed, through a combination of professional and voluntary work over nearly thirty years, in 1967) provided a powerful focus for the specific concerns of the Community: the integration of work and worship, politics and prayer, and the development of new forms of worship, of the common life, of youth work, of the ministry of healing, and of experiments in mission.

The Community today is a movement of some 200 members, 1,200 associates and 2,000 friends. It describes itself as 'an ecumenical community, within the Church of Scotland, of men and women seeking new ways of living the Gospel in today's world.' Its members are committed to a rule of daily prayer and Bible study, sharing and accounting for the use of their money and their time, meeting together, and action for peace and justice in the world.

The Community maintains three centres of work, worship, and the common life on Iona and Mull, and administrative offices in Glasgow.

For information on the Iona Community please contact:

The Iona Community, Pearce Institute, 840 Govan Road, Glasgow G51 3UU; Tel: 0141 445 4561; Fax: 0141 445 4295.

The following are available:

- Membership details
- A Deed of Covenant form
- Information about volunteering on Iona
- A catalogue of publications

Other titles available from Wild Goose Publications

SONGBOOKS with full music (titles marked * have companion cassettes)
GOD NEVER SLEEPS – PACK OF 12 OCTAVOS* John Bell (guest conductor)
COME ALL YOU PEOPLE, Shorter Songs for Worship* John Bell
PSALMS OF PATIENCE, PROTEST AND PRAISE* John Bell
HEAVEN SHALL NOT WAIT (Wild Goose Songs Vol.1)* John Bell and Graham Maule
ENEMY OF APATHY (Wild Goose Songs Vol.2) John Bell and Graham Maule
LOVE FROM BELOW (Wild Goose Songs Vol.3)* John Bell and Graham Maule
INNKEEPERS & LIGHT SLEEPERS* (for Christmas) John Bell
MANY & GREAT (Songs of the World Church Vol.1)* John Bell (ed./arr.)
SENT BY THE LORD (Songs of the World Church Vol.2)* John Bell (ed./arr.)
FREEDOM IS COMING* Anders Nyberg (ed.)
PRAISING A MYSTERY, Brian Wren
BRING MANY NAMES, Brian Wren

CASSETTES & CDs (titles marked † have companion songbooks)
Tape, GOD NEVER SLEEPS † John Bell (guest conductor)
Tape, COME ALL YOU PEOPLE † Wild Goose Worship Group
CD, PSALMS OF PATIENCE, PROTEST AND PRAISE † Wild Goose Worship Group
Tape, PSALMS OF PATIENCE, PROTEST AND PRAISE † Wild Goose Worship Group
Tape, HEAVEN SHALL NOT WAIT † Wild Goose Worship Group
Tape, LOVE FROM BELOW † Wild Goose Worship Group
Tape, INNKEEPERS & LIGHT SLEEPERS † (for Christmas) Wild Goose Worship Group
Tape, MANY & GREAT † Wild Goose Worship Group
Tape, SENT BY THE LORD † Wild Goose Worship Group
Tape, FREEDOM IS COMING † Fjedur
Tape, TOUCHING PLACE, A, Wild Goose Worship Group
Tape, CLOTH FOR THE CRADLE, Wild Goose Worship Group

DRAMA BOOKS
EH JESUS...YES PETER No. 1, John Bell and Graham Maule
EH JESUS...YES PETER No. 2, John Bell and Graham Maule
EH JESUS...YES PETER No. 3, John Bell and Graham Maule

PRAYER/WORSHIP BOOKS
THE PATTERN OF OUR DAYS, Liturgies and Resources for Worship, (ed.) K. Galloway
PRAYERS AND IDEAS FOR HEALING SERVICES, Ian Cowie
HE WAS IN THE WORLD, Meditations for Public Worship, John Bell
EACH DAY AND EACH NIGHT, Prayers from Iona in the Celtic Tradition, Philip Newell
IONA COMMUNITY WORSHIP BOOK, THE
WEE WORSHIP BOOK, A, Wild Goose Worship Group
WHOLE EARTH SHALL CRY GLORY, THE, George MacLeod

OTHER BOOKS
EXILE IN ISRAEL: A Personal Journey with the Palestinians, Runa Mackay
FALLEN TO MEDIOCRITY: CALLED TO EXCELLENCE, Erik Cramb
RE-INVENTING THEOLOGY AS THE PEOPLE'S WORK, Ian Fraser